RIVERDALE

Journal

by *Jenne Simon*

Scholastic Inc.

Photos ©: 1 top background and throughout: Samburova Maria/Shutterstock; 8 lipstick: victoriya89/iStockphoto; 28 stains and throughout: Monash/Shutterstock; 30 corners and throughout: Romanova Ekaterina/Shutterstock; 53 folder and throughout: David Smart/Shutterstock; 116 background and throughout: dastagir/Shutterstock.

ISBN 978-1-338-61098-7

10 9 8 7 6 5 4 3 2 1   20 21 22 23 24
Printed in China   171

First edition 2020
Book design by Jessica Meltzer
Illustrations by Gavin Reece

Tell Me All Your Secrets

In the fair town of Riverdale, things are never what they seem. Underneath the bubblegum lip gloss and drive-in double-date nights, everyone in town has secrets they'd kill to protect.

Innocent *Betty Cooper* doesn't want anyone to know about the murderous acts her own family has committed. *Archie Andrews* hides a thirst for violence inside his all-American BMOC image. *Jughead Jones* whispers orders to the Southside Serpents that he won't let anyone discover. And behind closed doors, *Veronica Lodge* plots to take down the biggest villain in town: her own father. But they aren't the only ones with secrets . . .

You have secrets, too. Harmless secrets. Juicy secrets. Dark secrets. And this journal is the perfect place to record them for posterity. Are you a clap-back queen like *Cheryl Blossom*? A boss babe like *Toni Topaz*? A center stage diva like *Josie McCoy*? Or maybe you're a sweetheart with the soul of a rebel like *Kevin Keller*.

If you want to *truly* know yourself, avoid the jingle jangle, dive into these interactive exercises, and write down all your dirtiest deeds. Maybe then you'll discover how *you* fit into this wicked little town.

All About Me

If you dare to play, get ready to bare your soul. No secret is too private to share, no sin too dirty to expose—at least not in the pages of this journal.

My favorite color is:
☐ Tiffany Blue   ☐ scarlet red   ☐ serpent green
☐ _____

My favorite class is:
☐ journalism   ☐ drama   ☐ PE   ☐ _____

I get around town by:
☐ bicycle   ☐ chauffeur   ☐ muscle car   ☐ _____

My future profession is:
☐ private eye   ☐ CEO   ☐ diplomat   ☐ _____

My style icon is:
☐ Coco Chanel   ☐ Martha Stewart   ☐ Lady Gaga
☐ _____

I am:
☐ ferocious   ☐ loyal   ☐ reckless   ☐ kind
☐ devious   ☐ generous   ☐ unique   ☐ passionate
☐ chaotic   ☐ hilarious   ☐ clever   ☐ _____

If you really want to know me, this is who I am:

_____
_____
_____
_____
_____
_____
_____
_____
_____
_____
_____
_____
_____
_____
_____
_____
_____
_____
_____
_____
_____
_____
_____
_____
_____
_____
_____
_____
_____

Would You Rather?

Extracurricular Edition

Ride with the Southside Serpents **or** cheer for the River Vixens' A squad?

Challenge Josie & the Pussycats to a battle of the bands **or** face the Riverdale Bulldogs on the football field?

Slurp milk shakes at Pop's Chock'lit Shoppe **or** dance all night at speakeasy La Bonne Nuit?

Join Dilton Doiley's Adventure Scouts troop **or** Kevin's production of Carrie: The Musical

"Listen up fives, a ten is speaking."

— Cheryl Blossom

There's More to the Story

Wannabe novelist Jughead Jones observes and records every dirty deed that goes down in Riverdale. But he's not the only one who can tell a good story. Take your cues from his prompts and decide where *you* want the story to go.

CHAPTER 1

Our story is about a small town and the people who live in the town. From a distance, it presents itself like so many other small towns all over the world: safe, decent, innocent. Get closer, though, and you start seeing the shadows underneath. The name of our town is Riverdale.

_____

_____

_____

_____

_____

_____

_____

_____

_____

_____

_____

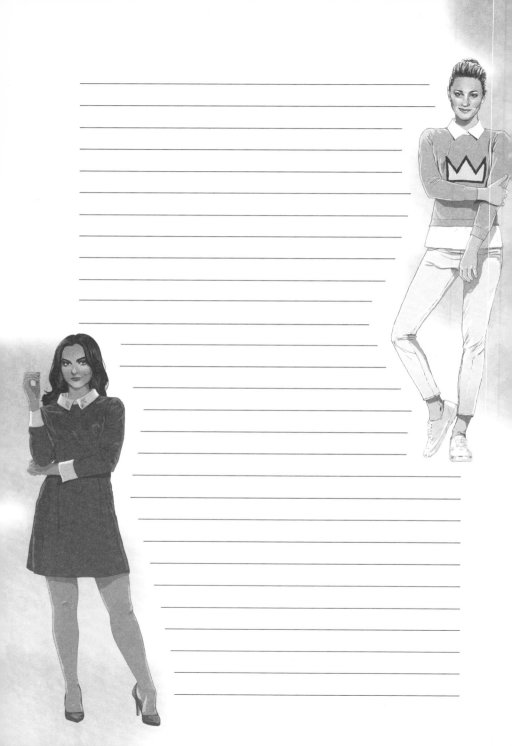

POP QUIZ

Are you a Betty or a Veronica?_____
_____

Who is scarier: a queen bee like Cheryl or a kingpin like Hiram Lodge?_____
_____

Are you outgoing like Josie McCoy or shy like Ethel Muggs?
_____
_____

Who's your ideal steady date: someone loyal like Archie or sensitive like Jughead? _____
_____

Are you distrustful like Toni Topaz or faithful like Evelyn Evernever? _____
_____

Who rains on your parade more: macho bros like Chuck Clayton or slick schemers like Nick St. Clair? _____
_____
_____
_____
_____
_____

Not Today, Inner Demons

Whether you're Dark Betty letting your deepest desires run free or Archie making a deal with the devil, everyone does things they aren't proud of. But that doesn't mean you're lost to the dark side. How do you quiet the voices in your head that urge you to be bad?

_____

_____

_____

_____

_____

_____

_____

_____

_____

_____

_____

_____

_____

_____

_____

_____

_____

_____

"I'm all about the beast within."

— Betty Cooper

_____
_____
_____
_____
_____
_____
_____
_____
_____
_____
_____
_____
_____
_____
_____
_____
_____
_____
_____
_____
_____
_____
_____
_____
_____
_____

Hot Off the Presses

Betty Cooper's newest article for this week's issue of *The Blue & Gold* is running late. Help her meet her deadline by filling in the blanks.

THE BLUE & GOLD

WEEKLY NEWSPAPER OF RIVERDALE HIGH

SECRET SOCIETY UNCOVERED

At Riverdale High School, _____ can earn you Saturday detention. But did you know that in the early 1990s, a group of our town's most _____ residents used those Saturdays to create a secret society known as the _____ Club? On one such weekend, they discovered a _____ game called _____ and began to play it with _____ results. Soon these students were hallucinating _____, breaking school rules, and pulling pranks like _____ _____, ultimately leading to the death of _____. Why? We may never know.

Article by
Betty Cooper

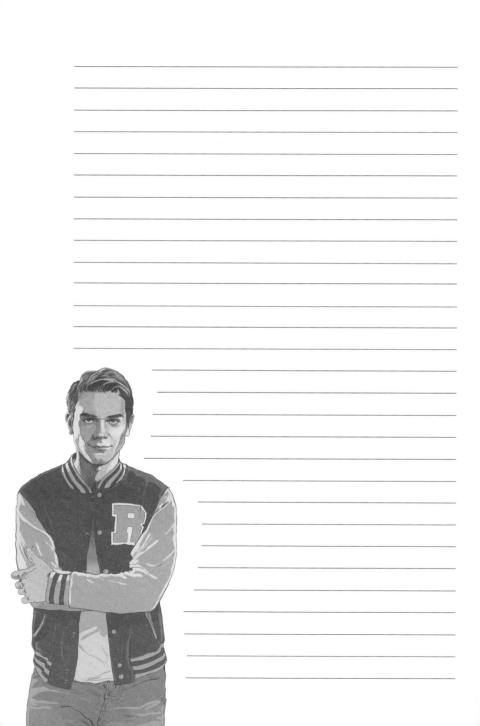

"Dance, Dance, Dance"

Music & Lyrics by Archie Andrews

I'm lost in the memory
Of the place where summer ends.
Late nights when this town gets small,
I'll be running through the streets again.

Let's make it hard to hold on.

Come on, turn the radio on,
And, honey, let's dance, dance, dance
For the rest of the night.
It's better left unsaid.

Yeah, come on, play the remix loud,
And, honey, we'll dance, dance, dance
For the rest of our lives.
I'm not ready to go yet.
We've got history to forget.

Gryphons and Gargoyles

Are you brave enough to play Riverdale's most dangerous role-playing game? Fill out this player profile to create your character.

Character Name: _____

Type:
- [ ] game master [ ] paladin [ ] thief
- [ ] sorcerer [ ] _____

Skill:
- [ ] strength [ ] intelligence [ ] personality
- [ ] magic [ ] _____

Caste:
- [ ] royalty [ ] cleric [ ] soldier
- [ ] peasant [ ] _____

Prioritize your attributes:

Vigor:	1	2	3	4	5	6
Agility:	1	2	3	4	5	6
Health:	1	2	3	4	5	6
Intellect:	1	2	3	4	5	6
Insight:	1	2	3	4	5	6
Magnetism:	1	2	3	4	5	6

Describe your character: _____
_____
_____
_____
_____
_____
_____
_____
_____

What's In a Name?

From Cheryl Bombshell to Archiekins, nicknames can reveal someone's true self. Use this nickname generator to find out what you'd go by in "the town with pep."

First Initial of Last Name

A, B   =   Big
C, D   =   Sister
E, F   =   Bride of
G, H   =   Little
I, J   =   Hardcore
K, L   =   Diamond
M, N   =   Doctor
O, P, Q =   General
R, S   =   Electric
T, U   =   Madame
V, W   =   Smooth
X, Y, Z =   Professor

Zodiac Sign

Aquarius = Hobo
Pisces   = Enigma
Aries   = Deadeye
Taurus   = Bijou
Gemini   = Fox
Cancer   = Maple
Leo   = Chanel
Virgo   = Topaz
Libra   = Serpent
Scorpio = Jingle Jangle
Sagittarius = Bulldog
Capricorn = Sweetwater

"Sardonic humor is just my way of relating to the world." — Jughead Jones

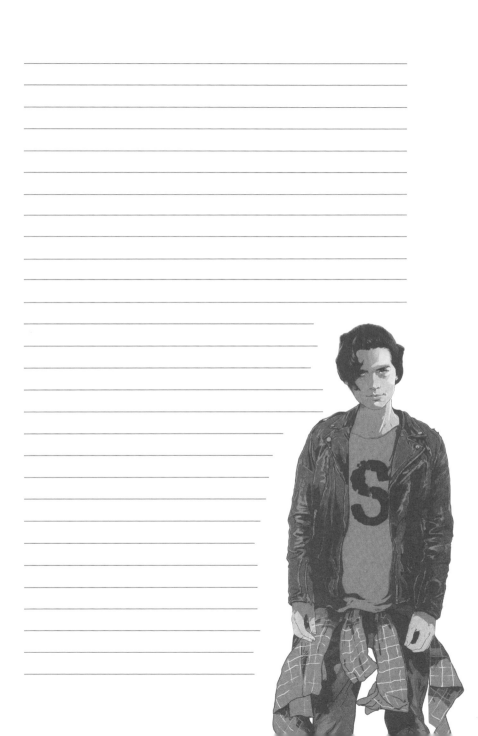

Top Ten Nightmare Phobias

Finish this list with your deepest fears.

1. Being stalked by the serial-killing Black Hood

2. Getting played by a rich playboy

3. Being betrayed by your bestie

4. Getting gaslighted by a creepy cult

5.

6.

7.

8.

9.

10.

M.A.S.H. Game

HOW TO PLAY: Pick a number between 5 and 20. Count out that many options on the page, then strike one out. Repeat, cycling through all of the options, until you're left with only one in each category. What will your future look like?

LIVES IN

Mansion (Thornhill)
Apartment (at the Pembrooke)
Shack (trailer at Sunnyside)
House (the Andrews place)

ROMANCE

Married to Archie
Dating Reggie
Hanging out with Toni
Living single

WORKOUT

Football drills
Prison boxing
Cheerleading jumps
Running in the woods

LOCATION

City
Suburbs
Country
Off the grid

HOBBY

Solving mysteries
Riding motorcycles
Playing guitar
Following politics

STYLE

Biker chic
Classic beauty
Clean-cut preppy
Vampy goddess

Who is the Black Hood?

Hiram Lodge—hates Fred Andrews, wants to sow discontent

Geraldine Grundy's abusive ex—he definitely has an ax to grind

Sheriff Keller—allowed station break-in and murder of Robert Phillips

Riverdale Reaper—could it be a copycat killer?

Joseph Svenson—wants revenge for slaughter of his family

Southside Serpents—are they trying to punish Northsiders?

~~Dad~~ Dad—IDK, but he's acting super crazy

"Can't we just liberate ourselves from the tired dichotomy of jock, artist? Can't we, in this post-James Franco world, be all things at once?"

— Veronica Lodge

_____

_____

_____

_____

_____

_____

_____

_____

_____

Secrets and Sins

If you dare to play, get ready to bare your soul. No secret is too private to share, no sin too dirty to expose—at least not in the pages of this journal.

My biggest secret is _____
_____
_____
_____

Why is it a secret? _____
_____
_____
_____

How long have you kept this secret? _____

The person who can never know about it is _____
_____

What would you do if they found out? _____
_____
_____

What would *they* do? _____
_____
_____

In Five Years . . .

Betty will be investigating _____

Archie will be promising _____

Veronica will be in charge of _____

Jughead will be moping about _____

Alice will be believing _____

Josie will be singing about _____

Cheryl will be feuding with _____

Hiram will be scheming _____

FP will be swearing _____

Penny will be betraying _____

I will be _____
_____
_____
_____
_____

THE SERPENTS' SECRET

THE SOUTHSIDE SERPENTS LIVE BY SIX UNBREAKABLE RULES:

#1:
A serpent never shows cowardice.

#2:
If a serpent's killed or imprisoned, their family will be taken care of.

#3:
No serpent stands alone.

#4:
No serpent is left for dead.

#5:
A serpent never betrays his own.

#6:
In unity, there is strength.

If you had your own ride-or-die gang, what would your unbreakable rules be?

#1 _____

_____

_____

#2 _____

_____

_____

#3 _____

_____

_____

#4 _____

_____

_____

#5 _____

_____

_____

#6 _____

_____

_____

#7 _____

_____

_____

"Fear.
It's the most basic,
the most human,
emotion. As kids,
we're afraid of
everything. The dark.
The boogeyman
under the bed.
And we pray for
morning. For the
monsters to go away.
Though they never
do. Not really."

— Jughead Jones

Cheryl Bombshell's Take No Prisoners playlist

"Diva"
by Beyoncé

"Nice for What"
by Drake

"Sorry Not Sorry"
by Demi Lovato

"There's Nothing Holdin' Me Back"
by Shawn Mendes

"What's My Name?"
by Rihanna

"Look What You Made Me Do"
by Taylor Swift

"The Greatest"
by Sia

"Royals"
by Lorde

REPEAT   STOP   PLAY   SKIP

Top Ten Epic Embarrassments

Finish this list with your deepest, most embarrassing secrets.

1. Reciting a personal poem out loud in English class
2. Getting handcuffed in a hot tub
3. Being tricked by a con artist who pretends to be family
4. Your crush spotting you in the middle of busting a (ridiculous) move
5.
6.
7.
8.
9.
10.

Outbreak!

Something sickening is plaguing Riverdale. Fill in the blanks to decide what poisonous dangers are in the air.

Memo

From: Principal Waldo Weatherbee

To: Students of Riverdale High

It has come to my attention that several members of the student body have suffered _____ as a side effect of a _____ outbreak. Until we know what is causing the _____, all sports and _____ activities are canceled until _____. Representatives from the Department of _____ & Restricted _____ will be inspecting the campus _____ to determine the severity of the situation. Be careful, students. Remember, _____ comes first.

"If you breathe, it's because I give you air."

— Cheryl Blossom

_____

_____

_____

_____

_____

_____

_____

_____

_____

_____

_____

_____

_____

_____

_____

_____

_____

_____

_____

_____

_____

_____

Archie's Prison Workout Routine

Workout	Reps
Barbell rows	
Squats	25 reps
Push-ups	25 reps
Sit-ups	25 reps
One-on-one bareknuckle boxing match	25 reps
Barbell rows	
Squats	15 reps
Push-ups	15 reps
Burpees	15 reps
Two-on-one fight club	15 reps

There's More to the Story

CHAPTER 3

Guilt, innocence. Good, evil. Life, death. As the shadows around Riverdale deepened, the lines that separated these polar opposites blurred and distorted. "I'm guilty," Cheryl said in biology class. But of what?

_____

_____

_____

_____

_____

_____

_____

_____

_____

_____

_____

_____

_____

_____

_____

_____

_____

_____

_____

_____

You Make Me Want to Hurl

Face it: Everyone's annoying. Even besties like Betty and Veronica drive each other a little nuts sometimes. List the pet peeves, major crises, and downright aggravating details that are making you crazy right now. Your secrets are safe here . . .

_____

_____

_____

_____

_____

You're Hilarious, Never Change

Now that you have that out of your system, there's no point in dwelling on spilled milk shake. The same friends who make you the craziest are also the people who cause the biggest smiles. List all of the sweet gestures, moronic jokes, and kind words that have come your way.

_____

_____

_____

_____

_____

"I don't follow the rules. I make them. And when necessary, I break them."

— Veronica Lodge

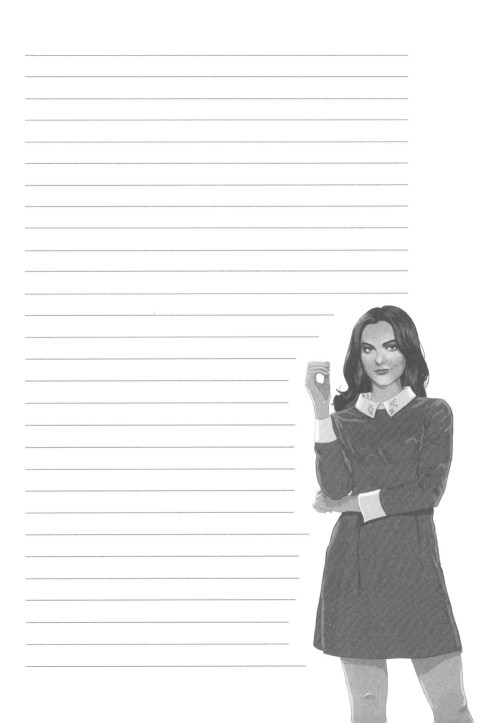

Yaaas, Queen!

Riverdale is full of badass babes who go after what they want and protect their own. Betty fights for justice, Veronica gets revenge, and Toni saves Cheryl from herself. Who is your real-life role model, and how do they inspire you?

_____
_____
_____
_____
_____
_____
_____
_____
_____
_____
_____
_____
_____
_____
_____
_____
_____
_____
_____
_____
_____

POP QUIZ

What's your favorite class?

A) English
B) math or science
C) PE
D) art or music
E) history

Which city would you want to live in?

A) New York
B) Tokyo
C) Riverdale
D) Paris
E) Toledo

What do you want to be when you grow up?

A) investigative journalist
B) someone powerful like a politician
C) fire chief
D) I don't care as long as I'm in charge
E) on parole

Pick your clique. You're:

A) a brain
B) popular
C) a jock
D) a drama queen
E) a rebel

How do you like your hamburgers?

A) classic, with cheese and pickles
B) spicy, with jalapeños
C) two patties, extra bacon
D) veggie burger with avocado
E) I'm not hungry

ANSWERS

Mostly A's: You're sweet and stubborn girl next door Betty Cooper.

Mostly B's: You're smooth-talking, charismatic, and totally magnetic Veronica Lodge.

Mostly C's: You're all-American hero and stand-up guy Archie Andrews.

Mostly D's: You're dramatic and intimidating, Cheryl Blossom.

Mostly E's: You're sensitive, soul-bearing Serpent and poet Jughead Jones.

Top Ten Juiciest Pieces of Gossip

Everyone likes to keep *some* things under wraps. But sometimes you have to spill the tea.

1. Riverdale's resident Rich Girl had a fling with the help.
2. G&G player Princess Etheline has an unrequited crush on Hellcaster.
3. The head cheerleader and her nemesis, the girl next door, are related.
4. A sultry songstress dropped her sweet pea for an all-American boy toy.
5.
6.
7.
8.
9.
10.

Clap Back!

Cheryl is the queen of the comeback, the high priestess of the cutting remark. She knows that the quickest way to end a fight isn't with your fists . . . it's using your words to shove a dagger in your enemy's heart. Here are a few of her most straight-up savage jabs:

"Hands off, Gollum!"

"You catatonic bimbos didn't vote for me!"

"You've got the vocabulary of a baked potato."

"That was a joke, you hobo."

"I think she's crazier than a serial killer on bath salts."

Now it's your turn. Sharpen your claws with the best clap-
backs you can think of.

_____

_____

_____

_____

_____

_____

_____

_____

_____

_____

_____

_____

_____

_____

_____

_____

_____

_____

_____

_____

_____

_____

_____

"I'm not the hero of any story. Lately, I've been going down this dark path."

— Archie Andrews

Would You Rather

Home Edition

Live independently at weathered Sunnyside Trailer Park **or** under Daddy's thumb in opulence at the Pembrooke?

Find a dead body in your living room **or** a planted murder weapon in your closet?

Attend a house party that spirals out of control **or** a slumber party where you aren't wanted?

Have separated parents who respect each other, like Archie **or** married parents who plot against each other, like Veronica?

If the Manolo Blahnik Fits . . .

Sure, everyone has flaws. But underneath it all, you have totally amazing qualities that make you a one-of-a-kind unicorn. For instance, Jughead is angsty but loyal, and Ethel is a little cray but super smart. So take a look in the mirror and list all of the things that make you as unique as a drama-free day in Riverdale.

_____

_____

_____

_____

_____

_____

_____

_____

_____

_____

_____

_____

_____

_____

_____

_____

_____

_____

_____

Betty's Rules for Investigating Like a True Nancy Drew

1. Bring a flashlight and camera.

2. Stealth is key, so don't get caught sneaking around.

3. Wear all black. It's flattering and hard to detect.

4. Use the buddy system—unless your buddy is the person you're digging up dirt on.

5. Keep detailed notes. You never know when you'll have to prove your accusations are true.

6. Keep quiet—loose lips sink ships.

7. Don't give up until you find out what's really going down.

8. Bobby pins are a must-have accessory—for keeping hair neat _and_ opening locked doors.

"There are some secrets that are so painful, you not only hide them from the world, but you hide them from yourself."

— Alice Cooper

_____
_____
_____
_____
_____
_____
_____
_____
_____
_____
_____

The Show Must Go On

As director of Riverdale's newest dramatic sensation, *Heathers: The Musical*, Kevin Keller has lots of words of encouragement for his cast and crew. Help motivate the team by filling in the blanks.

"I know we've all heard that staging a musical about _____ here at Riverdale High is _____, but as Freddie Mercury once said, 'The _____ must go on!' Cheryl will play the lead role of Heather Chandler, a _____ girl with _____ on the brain. It's perfect casting—totally _____! And our own Evelyn Evernever is joining me as _____. She'll help keep all of you _____ on task and off-book. She'll be hosting a _____ at the Sisters of Quiet Mercy after the performance. Now everyone, break a _____!"

Secret Shame

Everyone has a secret life they don't want the rest of the world to see—whether it's cruising the woods to meet up with strangers or putting on a wig to let their true selves come out to play. But even though shame is the gift that keeps giving, save it for Thanksgiving with your dysfunctional family. Own your guilty pleasures on the lines below.

_____

_____

_____

_____

_____

_____

_____

_____

_____

_____

_____

_____

_____

_____

_____

_____

_____

_____

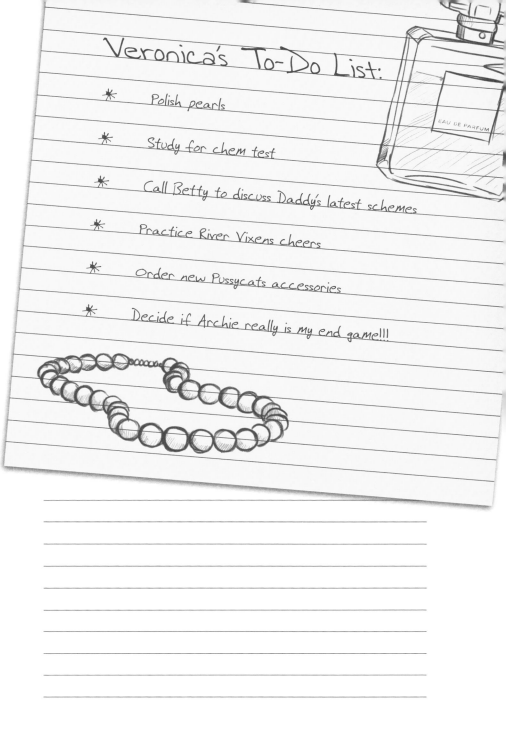

Veronica's To-Do List:

* Polish pearls

* Study for chem test

* Call Betty to discuss Daddy's latest schemes

* Practice River Vixens cheers

* Order new Pussycats accessories

* Decide if Archie really is my end game!!!

ARCHIE ANDREWS

CHERYL BLOSSOM

ELIZABETH COOPER

FORSYTHE P. JONES III

KEVIN KELLER

VERONICA LODGE

REGGIE MANTLE

JOSEPHINE MCCOY

ANTOINETTE TOPAZ

SUPERLATIVES

MOST LIKELY TO . . .	RIVERDALE	REALITY
Most likely to win the lottery		
Most likely to prank the principal		
Most likely to join a convent		
Most likely to get arrested		
Most likely to win an Oscar		
Most likely to join the FBI		
Most likely to lose their lunch		
Most likely to go off the grid		
Most likely to fight the power		
Most likely to travel the world		

"In real life, what you see is what you get."

— Kevin Keller

_____
_____
_____
_____
_____
_____
_____
_____
_____
_____
_____
_____
_____
_____
_____
_____
_____
_____
_____
_____
_____
_____

River Vixens Rallying Cry

The River Vixens cheer on the Riverdale Bulldogs on the football field, but they've also been known to support their friends in less conventional settings . . . like the prison yard. (Hey, everyone needs their own personal cheering section once in a while.) Write yourself a cheer to help give yourself a boost when you're feeling down in the dumps.

More About Me

My favorite writer is:

☐ Toni Morrison   ☐ Dr. Seuss   ☐ John Green

☐ _____

I believe in:

☐ justice   ☐ respect   ☐ love   ☐ _____

I respect my parents:

☐ true   ☐ false   ☐ _____

I like to wear:

☐ leather   ☐ cardigans   ☐ kitten heels   ☐ _____

My favorite sport is:

☐ boxing   ☐ archery   ☐ gossip   ☐ _____

I can be:

☐ scared   ☐ lonely   ☐ distracted   ☐ jealous   ☐ cruel
☐ rude   ☐ selfish   ☐ boring   ☐ _____

The thing I can never forgive under any circumstances is:

_____

_____

_____

_____

_____

There's More to the Story

CHAPTER 7

What makes a place feel like home? Is it warmth and familiarity? Some idealized, make-believe version of the American Dream? Is it love and acceptance? Or is it simple safety? Or, maybe it's none of those things, and it's a place where the captain of the football team is murdered. Or maybe it's just a forgotten closet under a well-trod staircase, where it's just you and the mice and the spiders.

_____

_____

_____

_____

_____

_____

_____

_____

_____

_____

_____

_____

_____

_____

_____

_____

_____

"The apple doesn't fall far from the tree, especially not when there's a snake curled up in its limbs." — Jughead Jones

Is there any hope for me and Moose?

-He's really hot

-He's got more demons than _The Exorcist_

-He can be really sweet

-His father's a psycho who has it out for me

-He came out for me

-He left Riverdale High

KK + MM = <3

Top Ten Signs of a Dysfunctional Family

Finish this list with *your* family's deepest secrets.

1. Your father killed your twin brother to keep the family drug business secret.
2. Big Sis is raising her babies in a cult and recruited your mom to join them.
3. Your dad frames your boyfriend for murder and gets him locked up.
4. Daddy Dearest is a stone-cold serial killer.

5. _____

6. _____

7. _____

8. _____

9. _____

10. _____

The Way We Were

Your memories are a garden. Tend the flowers to keep them bright and beautiful, and rip out the invasive weeds. Otherwise you can end up haunted by the secrets of the past. Just look at Betty's crazy-pants mother Alice Cooper.

Don't be like Alice. Record your fondest memories so you won't forget them. And let go of the ones that weigh you down.

_____

_____

_____

_____

_____

_____

_____

_____

_____

_____

_____

_____

_____

_____

_____

_____

_____

_____

_____

"I do everything for everyone. Everything to be perfect. The perfect daughter, the perfect sister, the perfect student. Can't I do this one thing for me?"

— Betty Cooper

_____
_____
_____
_____
_____
_____

Saturday Night In, Choni-Style

7:30 p.m. Dinner catered by the Five Seasons

8:30 p.m. Dessert—since we're cuckoo-bananas for each other, obvi banana splits are on the menu

9:00 p.m. Netflix binge

11:15 p.m. Plan coordinating outfits for the week

12:00 a.m. Smooch while organizing a field trip for the Serpent ladies

Crushing It

Can you feel them? The butterflies in your stomach every time the BMOC or that soulful loner passes you in the hallway? Or the feeling that your heart might burst when that special someone smiles at you across the crowded cafeteria? That's a crush, my friend, and everyone gets 'em.

Do you go for supportive sweeties like Toni Topaz, or good-time guys like Reggie Mantle? No matter your flavor of choice, knowing *why* you like someone can help you decide if it's the real deal or just a passing flirtation. Use this space to explore exactly what you like about your hopeful honey-bunny.

Would You Rather

Romance Edition

Take a date to a flick at the Bijou **or** go wild at the Whyte Wyrm?

Have a fling with someone who's already spoken for **or** someone from the wrong side of the tracks?

Crush on the boy/girl next door in secret **or** have your feelings out in the open, but unrequited?

Have one meant-to-be endgame love **or** try out every flavor on the menu?

The Right Ways to Procrastinate

- Make decorations for the Homecoming Dance committee
- _____
- _____
- Research your long-lost sibling to find out where he's been
- _____
- _____
- _____
- Break your boyfriend out of juvie
- _____
- _____
- _____
- _____
- Protest conversion therapy at creepy youth home run by sociopathic nuns
- _____
- _____
- Write in your journal
- _____
- _____
- _____
- Write an email to the parent you rarely see
- _____
- _____
- _____

"From now on, we're protecting our own."

— Archie Andrews

Once upon a time...

. . . in the kingdom of Eldervair, a beautiful Upper East Side princess named Veronica came to live among the peasants. She was *Breakfast at Tiffany's*; they were In *Cold Blood*. Yet somehow she came to befriend sweet Lady Elizabeth, a poetic jester called Forsythe, and Sir Archibald the Muscled, a brave paladin who won her over with his loyalty and lustrous ginger locks. But an evil had invaded Eldervair—Princess Veronica's father, King Hiram, who would stop at nothing to destroy all happiness in the kingdom. Luckily, Princess Veronica was crafty and had a plan to stop the brutish King, and she'd need her new friends' help.

Finish this tale to help the Fellowship of Eldervair devise a plot to complete their quest: saving the kingdom.

_____

_____

_____

_____

_____

_____

_____

_____

Style File

Our clothing tells the world all about us. Veronica wears designer labels that make her feel classic, polished, and ready to take on any obstacles in her path. Betty's no-nonsense ponytail is practical, cute, and totally iconic. Ethel's sensible sweaters and flats show she has more on her mind than fashion. Toni wears a leather jacket to show her gang allegiance. And Cheryl wears whatever she wants—as long as it's in her signature red. Use these pages to draw some outfits that show the world who *you* really are.

I Feel Your Pain

Whether you've had an unrequited crush on the boy next door like Betty or felt neglected by your parents like Cheryl, empathy for others is one of the things that makes us all human. And we can all relate to at least *some* of the stuff going on in Riverdale. Do any of these situations strike a chord with something going on in your life?

Ethel believes she deserves the lead role in *Carrie: the Musical*, but she doesn't get it. _____

_____

Archie struggles with losing his dad. _____

_____

Sweet Pea has a hard time accepting the Southside Serpents' new leader. _____

_____

Josie has to decide between either doing what's best for her band, or doing what's best for her solo career. _____

_____

Cheryl is jealous that her brother was her parents' favorite. _____

_____

"I'm in the mood for chaos."

— Cheryl Blossom

_____
_____
_____
_____
_____
_____
_____
_____
_____
_____
_____
_____
_____
_____
_____
_____
_____
_____
_____
_____
_____
_____
_____
_____
_____

The Gargoyle King

A Poem by Ethel Muggs

For quests and candy, I will comply.
I am your favorite child.
I know not what you plan for me,
With messages coded and rumors wild.

My King, my savior—
Guide me through the night.
Bless me with your darkness,
Gift me with your flight.

Revenge Is Sweet

When someone does you wrong, it's human nature to want a little payback. See Archie's vendetta against the Black Hood for shooting his father or Jughead's ousting of Penny Peabody from the Serpents after she blackmailed him.

An eye for an eye, and all that. Just be careful that the punishment doesn't outweigh the crime. Turning the other cheek may not make you feel better, but it does come with certain bragging rights . . .

Have *you* ever wanted revenge?

_____

_____

_____

_____

_____

_____

_____

_____

_____

_____

_____

_____

_____

_____

There's More to the Story

CHAPTER 16

Every fairy tale comes with the same warning: Good children should never go into the woods alone. Stray from the path and who knows what you'll encounter. A hungry wolf. A handsome devil. Or maybe something worse.

_____

_____

_____

_____

_____

_____

_____

_____

_____

_____

_____

_____

_____

_____

_____

_____

_____

_____

_____

_____

_____

Pay It Forward

Sometimes the only way to change the world is to do a little good. So when someone has your back—whether that means loaning you their killer heels, trying to clear your good name, or saving you from a serial killer (or even just from yourself)—don't let the kindness die with one small act. Pass it on to someone else. Any ideas on how you can do that?

_____

_____

_____

_____

_____

_____

_____

_____

_____

_____

_____

_____

_____

_____

_____

_____

_____

_____

_____

"You wanted fire? Sorry. My specialty is ice."

— Veronica Lodge

_____
_____
_____
_____
_____
_____
_____
_____
_____
_____
_____
_____
_____
_____
_____
_____
_____
_____
_____
_____
_____
_____
_____

Kiss, Marry, Cut Off

Three names. Three choices. No exceptions. Who do you kiss? Who do you marry? Who do you cut off forever?

Veronica Lodge	Betty Cooper	Cheryl Blossom
_____	_____	_____
Sweet Pea	Fangs Fogarty	Jughead Jones
_____	_____	_____
Reggie Mantle	Chuck Clayton	Archie Andrews
_____	_____	_____
Ethel Muggs	Evelyn Evernever	Polly Cooper
_____	_____	_____
Joaquin DeSantos	Kevin Keller	Moose Mason
_____	_____	_____

What Are You Afraid of?

Rank the following terrifying situations from 1 ("I'm barely shaking in my saddle shoes") to 10 ("I'm so scared, I'm going to be in therapy for the rest of my life!").

____ You're trapped inside a hidden bunker in the woods—and no one knows you're missing.

____ Daddy cuts off your allowance. No more designer bags or sick rides for you.

____ You're drag racing against a ghoulish gang, and losing could be deadly.

____ You're sneaking into an abandoned house to confront a killer who knows everything about you.

____ Developers buy up your neighborhood so they can totally demolish it.

____ A secret admirer leaves you a gift: a human heart. If they can't have you, no one can.

____ Your brother turns out to be a lying grifter with a questionable job history.

____ The boy you like spreads nasty rumors about you.

____ You tell your girlfriend you love her, and she doesn't say it back.

____ You come home from school to find a dead body in your living room.

What are you most afraid of? Record your deepest fears here.

_____

_____

_____

_____

_____

_____

_____

_____

_____

_____

_____

_____

_____

_____

_____

_____

_____

_____

_____

_____

_____

_____

_____

_____

_____

_____
_____
_____
_____

"All For Me"

Music & Lyrics by Archie Andrews and Valerie Brown

Paintings on her skin, colors in her hair,
Come around the corner, make you stop and stare.
But she don't hit her mark 'cause she don't really care,
What you think about her, think about her.

Moving through the streets, she travels on her own,
'Cause she don't need nobody else to let her know
How to go 'bout living or where she should go.
And if you try to tell her what to do, she'll say:

I don't care what you want me to be,
'Cause it ain't for you, no,
It's all for me.

Get a lot of people say they try to help,
But they don't know her story, they just try to sell
A cookie cutter recipe for living well.
But they don't take the time to stop and listen.

Covering her ears she pushes on alone
'Cause she don't need nobody else to let her know
How to go 'bout living or where she should go.
And if you try to slow her down, she'll scream:

I don't care what you want me to be,
'Cause it ain't for you, no,
It's all for me.

They tried to keep her down,
But she won't stop for no man.
They tried to shake her down.
Nothing can shake her.
Nothing can shake her.

I don't care what you want me to be,
'Cause it ain't for you, no,
It's all for me.

Hot Off the Presses

Betty is writing an article about the Farm, the creepy cult that has hypnotized her family. Help her meet her deadline by filling in the blanks.

THE BLUE & GOLD

WEEKLY NEWSPAPER OF RIVERDALE HIGH

FARM OR HARM?

A _____ called the Farm has recently moved to Riverdale. With headquarters at the _____ that formerly housed the Sisters of Quiet Mercy, members of the Farm say their mission is to spread peace, support, and _____.

But Martha, a former _____ of the group, reports their purpose is much darker. "The Farm believes that if _____ can get close enough to _____,

you'll see the truth," Martha says. The group's _____ leader, Edgar Evernever, claims that members must survive an extreme _____ in order to achieve in order to achieve _____. This reporter thinks she smells a _____.

Article by
Betty Cooper

"Archie is swell. But like most millennial straight men, he needs to be told what he wants."

— Kevin Keller

_____
_____
_____
_____
_____
_____
_____
_____
_____
_____
_____
_____
_____
_____
_____
_____

Insecurity Check

Jughead thinks he's a weirdo. Betty wonders if her dark side is too much for anyone to handle. Heck, even Cheryl worries that she might be unlovable. Truth is, everyone feels insecure some of the time. But we can't let the dark side win.

Use Toni's encouraging words to her girl Cheryl as an example of how you can pull yourself back from nasty thoughts that can get you down:

"Cheryl, I am so sorry. But you have to know your mother's wrong. You're not loveless. You're not deviant. Okay? You're . . . sensational."

Now confront your own harshest thoughts about yourself by writing mantras to get you through the darkest days.

_____

_____

_____

_____

_____

_____

_____

_____

_____

Hail to the Chief

Elections in Riverdale are more heated than a hot tub in Hades. Whether it's Archie and Veronica battling it out for student council president or Hermione Lodge trashing Fred Andrews in her bid to be the town's next mayor, you can bet the candidates will do anything to bring home a victory. Imagine you're running for office. What promises would you make to win the day? Would you ever break them?

_____

_____

_____

_____

_____

_____

_____

_____

_____

_____

_____

_____

_____

_____

_____

_____

_____

_____

Top Ten Fantasy Dates

Finish this list with your deepest secret desires for you and your boo's next date night.

1. Taking in a flick at the Twilight Drive-In

2. Boating down Sweetwater River

3. Clubbing at the Roving Eye

4. Splitting a milk shake at Pop's Chock'lit Shoppe

5.

6.

7.

8.

9.

10.

Last Will and Testament

When a loved one—or a hated one, as the case may be—passes away, who they bequeath their prized possessions to can make for some pretty interesting reading. Just ask Cheryl. When her father, Clifford, died, she inherited the bulk of her family's money, leaving her mother twisting in the wind. Now it's your turn. Think of the people in your life you'd most like to reward and the ones you'd most like to let rot, and draft a will letting them have their due.

_____

_____

_____

_____

_____

_____

_____

_____

_____

_____

_____

_____

_____

_____

_____

_____

I, _____, being of sound mind and body, on this day, the _____ of _____ in the year _____, do hereby inscribe the terms of my last will and testament.

To _____, for their loyalty and faith, I leave _____.

_____, will receive _____ for their love and support.

Because of _____, I leave _____ to _____.

To _____, who betrayed me, I leave _____.

_____ deserves _____, for the time they _____.

For their honesty and respect, I leave _____ to _____.

And to _____, I leave absolutely nothing. They know what they did.

"You can't go through life trying not to get hurt."

— Archie Andrews

_____
_____
_____
_____
_____
_____
_____
_____
_____
_____
_____
_____
_____
_____
_____
_____
_____
_____
_____

Would You Rather

Living on the Edge Edition

Take on a serial killer with the help of your friends **or** do it solo to protect them?

Play cat-and-mouse with the Black Hood? **or** a deadly game of Gryphons and Gargoyles?

Wander through Fox Forest after dark **or** swim among the bodies floating in Sweetwater River?

Face off against a mobster like Papa Poutine **or** a crooked cop like Sheriff Minetta?

There's More to the Story

CHAPTER 17

Everyone's afraid to say it, so let me be the first. There is a serial killer amongst us. San Francisco had the Zodiac. New Orleans had the Axeman. Texarkana, Texas, had the Phantom Killer. The list goes on and on. Add to their ranks Riverdale's very own psychopath, the Black Hood.

_____

_____

_____

_____

_____

_____

_____

_____

_____

_____

_____

_____

_____

_____

_____

_____

_____

_____

Missing Pieces

When Betty Cooper gets mad, the world better watch out. Fill in the blanks to decide how she's going to take down the latest creep to get in her way.

_____

_____

_____

_____

_____

_____

_____

_____

_____

"You think you're the only _____ who

can scare people by being _____? You may

have fooled_____, but not me. I'm gonna

bring you down. Because I catch bad _____.

I caught _____.

I caught _____.

And I caught _____.

And you know what they all have in common? They're

_____. Consider yourself warned."

"You're welcome to challenge me, but you'll lose."

— Cheryl Blossom

I See the Future

What do you want to do with your life? Are you itching to get married and become a helicopter parent to two (or, surprise, three) kids like Alice Cooper? Do you want to start your own construction business, or run an empire? Maybe you'd rather lead a band of rebels, fight crime, or open an underground club. Or maybe you'd rather just sit back and watch some really juicy TV. No matter what your life plans are, take it from the citizens of "the town with pep": setting goals and taking steps to achieve them is the only surefire way to get you where you want to go.

Goal: _____
☐ Step 1: _____
☐ Step 2: _____
☐ Step 3: _____

Goal: _____
☐ Step 1: _____
☐ Step 2: _____
☐ Step 3: _____

Goal: _____
☐ Step 1: _____
☐ Step 2: _____
☐ Step 3: _____